How to Use This

The **Teaching Versions** of *Elemen* help you guide students to become fluent readers. Because fluency is not an isolated skill but is closely linked to word knowledge and comprehension, each **Teaching Version** contains the following types of teacher support:

- **Fluency teaching suggestions** to help students become proficient in reading with expression (prosody).

- **Word knowledge teaching suggestions** to build students' proficiency in reading words and understanding their structure and meanings. The word knowledge suggestions address high-frequency words, decoding skills, structural analysis skills, and knowledge of word meanings.

- **Sentence comprehension questions** to help students develop literal comprehension at the sentence level.

- **Story comprehension questions** to help students develop inferential comprehension. Additional comprehension questions are provided in the **Teacher's Lesson Folder**.

After students complete the repeated reading activities outlined on page 1.12 of the **Teacher's Lesson Folder**, use the reduced **Student Book** pages and teaching suggestions in this **Teaching Version** to provide explicit page-by-page instruction.

Why Bears Have Short Tails

■ **Fluency Focus**

Expression Conveying feelings, mood, or characterization

Punctuation Recognizing that quotation marks signal character speech

Punctuation Observing junctures indicated by commas

■ **Word Knowledge Focus**

Word Meanings Words with multiple meanings

High-Frequency Words (Boldface words appear in each book of the theme.)

a, about, again, all, almost, **always**, am, and, are, back, be, big, but, came, can, **change**, cold, come, could, day, did, eat, for, good, got, had, **hard**, have, he, him, his, home, I, in, is, it, keep, like, little, long, made, me, must, my, **never**, next, no, not, now, of, off, on, one, out, pulled, put, river, said, so, some, soon, start, still, that, the, then, they, **time**, to, today, under, up, very, want, was, well, went, were, when, why, will, would, yes, you, your

■ **Sentence Comprehension Focus**

Identifying speaker

■ **Story Comprehension Focus**

Making predictions

Why Bears Have Short Tails

Written by Hiawyn Oram
Illustrated by Beccy Blake

Harcourt
Supplemental Publishers
Rigby • Steck-Vaughn
www.steck-vaughn.com

Getting Started

To begin, read the title page aloud or invite a volunteer to do so.

Book Summary

At the beginning of this *pourquoi* tale, Bear has a long tail. During a hard winter, Bear steals Fox's fish. Fox teaches Bear a lesson by convincing him to fish with his tail in a river. Bear's tail freezes and breaks off in the river. Now all bears have short tails.

■ Fluency

Guide students to connect the events in the story with the way their voice should sound as they read (for example, upbeat in some parts and suspenseful in others).

Model reading the first three lines in an upbeat manner, pausing at the commas. Read the last sentence with antici-pation of difficult times to come. Have students listen for places where you pause as you read.

Explain that some sentences have a comma after a group of words at the beginning of the sentence. Tell students that the comma signals a brief pause. Have students read the page chorally the same way you did.

■ Word Knowledge

Have a volunteer write the theme high-frequency words (*always*, *change*, *hard*, *never*, *time*) in a list on the board. Then have students read the words chorally. Ask which words are on page 2.

Long ago, Bear was not like he is today.
Back then, he had a long tail.
Back then, he was always hungry.
Then a long, hard winter came.

2

■ Sentence Comprehension

Ask *What was Bear like long ago?* (He had a long tail and was always hungry.)

It got cold.
Then it got colder.
The river turned to ice.
Bear could not fish.

3

■ Sentence Comprehension

Ask *Why can't Bear fish?*
(The river has turned to
ice.)

■ Fluency

Have students read the page
silently and think about what
Bear might be feeling and
how to convey his feelings
as they read aloud. Lead
students in an echo reading
of the page, expressing
sadness at Bear's situation.

■ Word Knowledge

Point out the words "hard"
on page 2 and "turned" on
page 3. Explain that they are
words with more than one
meaning. Write each word
and its definitions on the
board (*hard*: "not soft," "not
easy," "with great force";
turned: "moved in a circle,"
"changed direction,"
"changed"). Ask which
meaning is used for each
word (*hard*: "not easy";
turned: "changed").

Tell students that the word
fish also has more than one
meaning. Ask what it means
on page 3 ("to catch fish").

All the animals were hungry—
well, almost all the animals.

4

■ Fluency

Have students read the page silently to determine how the animals probably feel about being hungry (sad). Model how the tone should change for the second line. Focus students' attention on the dash and explain that it signals a brief pause, much like a comma.

Lead students in an echo reading of the page.

■ Sentence Comprehension

Ask *Which animals are always hungry?* (almost all)

Fox was never hungry.
He always had fish.
He always had big fish and little fish.
He always had long fish and short fish.

5

Read the page in a flat mono-tone, then with a boastful tone, emphasizing "never," "always," "fish," "big," "little," "long," and "short." Ask students which reading was better and have them describe how Fox felt (proud, happy). Have students read the page chorally in the same way you did.

■ Sentence Comprehension

Ask   *Why is Fox never hungry?* (He always has fish.)

■ Word Knowledge

Have a volunteer lead students in an echo reading of the theme high-frequency words on the board. Ask students which words are on the page.

Write the following sentences from pages 3 and 5 on the board:

Bear could not fish.
He always had fish.

Ask students to tell what "fish" means in the first sentence ("to catch fish") and in the second ("a water animal that breathes with gills").

■ Fluency

Point out the introductory phrase "One day" and the comma that follows it. Ask students how they should read the sentence (pause at the comma).

Have students read the page silently and think about how Bear feels at this point in the story. Guide students to conclude Bear feels satisfied or happy because he is not hungry anymore. Encourage students to use their voice to convey this feeling as they read aloud.

■ Word Knowledge

Have students read the first and third sentences to determine the meaning of "fish" in each.

One day, Fox went out to fish.
Bear went to Fox's home.
He stole a big fish.
The big fish was good.

6

■ Sentence Comprehension

Ask *How does Bear get a fish?* (He steals it from Fox's home.)

The next day, Bear went back.
He stole a little fish.
Bear was about to eat the little fish
when Fox came back!

7

■ **Fluency**

Point out the comma after "The next day." Ask students what the comma signals (a brief pause).

Have students read the page silently to determine Bear's feelings. Help them conclude that Bear is probably feeling good, even greedy. Ask them which sentence signals that Bear's feelings are about to change (the last). Encourage students to experiment with reading the last sentence to let a reader know that exciting action is about to happen.

■ **Sentence Comprehension**

Ask *What happens when Bear steals fish on the second day?* (Fox comes back.)

■ Fluency

Have students read the page silently and tell how Bear feels. Point out the quotation marks and explain that they signal that a character is speaking. Guide students to see that Bear is speaking and that his words show that he is feeling sorry for stealing from Fox. Also point out the commas as signals to pause briefly. Encourage students to use their voice to show Bear's feelings as they read the page aloud.

■ Word Knowledge

Have students read aloud the list of theme high-frequency words on the board. Ask them to find *change* and *never* on the page. Ask volunteers to read aloud the sentences containing the words.

Bear said, "Fox, I am very sorry.
I want to change.
Teach me to fish under the ice.
Then I will never steal your fish again."

8

■ Sentence Comprehension

Ask   *Who says, "I want to change"?* (Bear)

Fox asked, "Teach you?
Oh, yes, Bear.
I will teach you, and you will change."

9

■ Fluency

Focus students' attention on the quotation marks and ask students what they signal (that a character is speaking). Point out the words "Fox asked" and ask who speaks on this page (Fox). Have students point out the places where a reader should pause when reading the page (at each comma and period).

Ask students to read the page silently to determine how Fox feels (seems forgiving, but has a plan in mind). Invite volunteers to model reading the page with expression to convey Fox's feelings.

■ Sentence Comprehension

Ask *Who speaks on this page?* (Fox)

■ Word Knowledge

Have students refer to the list of theme high-frequency words on the board and find the one on the page. Then have them read aloud the sentence containing the word.

■ Fluency

Ask students if a character speaks on this page and how they know (yes; quotation marks). Help students determine who is speaking by explaining that "He" in the third sentence refers to Fox.

Have students read the page silently and tell how Bear is probably feeling (happy). Guide them to understand that Bear is probably happy because he thinks Fox has forgiven him and because he's going to learn to fish.

Encourage students to read with a happy voice as you lead them in an echo reading of the page.

Bear and Fox went to the river.
Fox made a hole in the ice.
He said, "Put your tail in the hole.
You will feel the fish pulling your tail."
Bear put his long tail in the hole.

10

■ Sentence Comprehension

Ask *Who tells Bear to put his tail in the hole?* (Fox)

10

Fox asked, "Can you feel the fish pulling?"
Bear said, "Yes, I can!
They are pulling hard.
I am catching some fish!
Can I pull up my tail now?"

11

Sentence Comprehension

Ask *Who asks, "Can you feel the fish pulling?"* (Fox)

Fluency

Have students identify the speakers and each speaker's words. Point out the variety of punctuation marks on the page and talk with students about what each signals.

Read the page aloud. Then ask how the characters feel. (Fox is happy; Bear is even happier than before, and excited.) Encourage students to convey these feelings as they read the page aloud in unison.

Word Knowledge

Invite a volunteer to point to *hard* in the list of theme high-frequency words on the board. Then have students read aloud the sentence that contains the word.

Have volunteers read aloud the definitions of *hard* on the board. Then ask students which meaning is used on the page ("with great force").

■ Fluency

Have students read along silently as you read the page two times—first in a monotone and then with a happy tone. Ask students which reading conveyed the character's feelings. Have them identify places where you paused and the corresponding punctuation mark for each pause.

Ask students if a character is speaking on this page and how they know (yes; quotation marks). Have students identify the speaker (Fox).

■ Word Knowledge

Spell the high-frequency word *time* aloud and ask students to find the word on the page. Have a volunteer read aloud the sentence containing the word.

Fox said, "Oh, no!
It is not time.
Keep fishing.
I will come back soon."

12

■ Sentence Comprehension

Ask *Who is going to come back soon?* (Fox)

But Fox did not come back soon.
He did not come back for a long time
Bear could feel the fish pulling his tail.
He said, "It must be time now.
I will pull up my tail."

13

Sentence Comprehension

Ask   *Which character speaks on this page?* (Bear)

Fluency

Ask students if any of the characters are speaking on this page and how they know (yes; quotation marks).

Have students read the page silently. Remind them that the story is mostly about Bear and ask how Bear is feeling on this page (excited; anxious to catch the fish). Lead students in an echo reading of the page. Use a sad tone for the first two lines and an excited or nervous one for the others.

Word Knowledge

Have a volunteer read aloud the theme high-frequency words on the board. Then ask which word from the list is on the page and how many times it appears (two).

Have students refer to the list of theme high-frequency words on the board and identify the one that appears on the page. Have them read aloud the two sentences that contain the word.

Have volunteers read the definitions of *hard* on the board. Ask which meaning is used on the page ("with great force").

Bear pulled.
His tail would not come out of the river.
Bear pulled hard.
He pulled so hard that his tail came off!
It was frozen in the ice!

14

■ **Sentence Comprehension**

Ask *What happens to Bear's tail?* (It freezes in the ice, and it comes off.)

Fox came back.
He laughed, "Ha! Ha! Ha!
I said you would change, and you did!
Fish were not pulling on your tail.
The river was freezing it.
Never steal my fish again!"

15

Sentence Comprehension

Ask *Who says, "Never steal
my fish again!"?* (Fox)

Fluency

Have students read pages
14–15 silently and determine
how they should be read. Ask
them to think about what is
happening and how the characters are feeling. (Bear is
stuck, and Fox is laughing.
Bear is scared, and Fox is
very happy.) Allow students
to experiment with how they
can convey Fox's glee.

Lead the class in a choral
reading of the two pages.

Word Knowledge

Point out the third and last
sentences and ask students
to find the theme high-
frequency word in each.

■ Fluency

Point out the comma after "Today" in the third sentence. Ask students how they should read this sentence (with a pause at the comma).

Ask students to determine how Bear feels (sorry). Model changing the voice from sorry for the first two sentences to a more upbeat tone in the last two. Read the last sentence with strong feeling and emphasize "never." Have students imitate your reading.

■ Word Knowledge

Have students find the word that is a form of *change* ("changed"). Then have them find the theme high-frequency word in the last sentence.

Bear was very sorry.
That winter changed him forever.
Today, all bears have short tails.
And they never feel hungry in winter!

16

■ Sentence Comprehension

Ask *Does Bear learn a lesson? How do you know?* (Bear does learn a lesson. At the end of the story, he is sorry.)

■ Story Comprehension

Ask *How does Bear probably feel about Fox at the end of the story?* (Answers will vary.)

Ask *The next time someone steals Fox's fish, what will he probably do?* (teach him or her a lesson)

Ask *Will Bear steal Fox's fish the next winter?* (probably not)

Ask *What might Bear do the next time it is very cold in the winter and he can't fish?* (Answers will vary.)

Bear could feel the fish pulling his tail. 8

He said, "It must be time now. 15

I will pull up my tail." 21

Bear pulled. 23

His tail would not come out of the river. 32

Bear pulled hard. 35

He pulled so hard that his tail came off! 44

It was frozen in the ice! 50

Fox came back. 53

He laughed, "Ha! Ha! Ha! 58

I said you would change, and you did! 66

Fish were not pulling on your tail. 73

The river was freezing it. 78

Never steal my fish again!" 83

Bear was very sorry. 87

That winter changed him forever. 92

■ Fluency Flip Page

The **Fluency Flip Page** of the **Student Book** contains a passage from the book to facilitate timed reading. For more information on timed reading and other ways of assessing fluency, see the **Teacher's Lesson Folder**.